7243 5 96835 2 2

STEREO

JOSS STONE
THE SOUL SESSIONS

PUBLISHED 2004

© INTERNATIONAL MUSIC PUBLICATIONS LIMITED

Griffin House, 161 Hammersmith Road, London, England W6 8BS

Music arranged and engraved by **ARTEMIS MUSIC LTD**
(www.artemismusic.com)

Art Direction & Design: **DAVID GORMAN** & **BRYAN LASLEY**
for **HACKMART**, Inc.
Photography: **CHARLES ALLEN SMITH**, **KAREN FUCHS**, **ROGER MOENKS**
& **LAURENT ALFIERI**

THE CHOKIN' KIND

Words and Music by Harlan Howard

Gently, with a beat

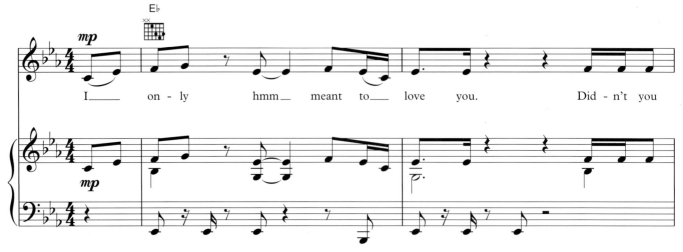

I ___ on-ly hmm___ meant to___ love you. Did-n't you

know it ba - by, did-n't you know it? And why___ couldn't you be con-

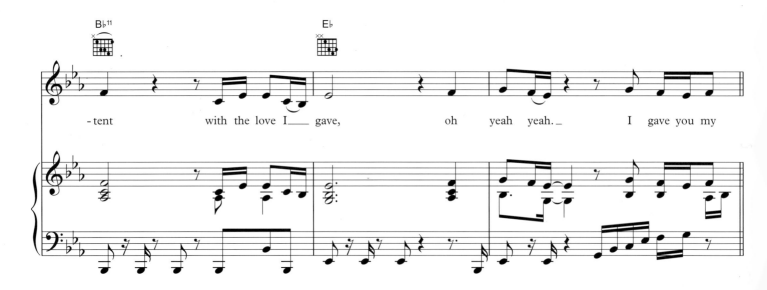

-tent with the love I___ gave, oh yeah yeah.___ I gave you my

SUPER DUPER LOVE
(ARE YOU DIGGIN' ON ME?) Pt. 1

Words and Music by Willie Garner

Am7
G
Am7
ba - by. See, I'm try - ing to tell you your love is sup - er du - per oh.
G
N.C.
Sup - er yes it is, yes it is. Your love is your love is
sup - er. Are you dig - gin' on me 'cause I'm dig - gin' on you
I'm just try - ing to tell you oh this love is sup - er du - per, wait a min - ute.

FELL IN LOVE WITH A BOY

Words and Music by Jack White

1. Fell in love with a boy.____ I
2. Red____ hair with a curl,____ mellow
3. *Guitar Solo ad lib* .
4. *See block lyric*

fell in love once, and al - most com - plete - ly.____ He's in love with the world,____ and some -
roll for the fla - vor and eyes for peep - ing.__ Can't_ keep a - way from the boy, the two

-times these feel - ings can be so mis - lead - ing.__ He turns_ and says, "Are you al - right?" Oh I
sides of my brain need to have a meet - ing.__ Can't think of a - ny - thing to do.____ My

ah.

Ah,

ah.

Bbm⁷

4.

F⁷

Don't go tell-ing no more, don't go tell-ing no more,

3. Guitar Solo

Can't think of anything to do.
My left brain knows all love is fleeting.
He's just looking for something new,
I said it once before but it bears repeating.

4. Fell in love with a boy.
I fell in love once, and almost completely.
He's in love with the world,
And sometimes these feelings can be so misleading.
He turns and says, "Are you alright?"
Oh I must be fine, 'cause me heart's still beating.
Come and kiss me by the riverside,
Sarah says it's cool she don't consider it cheating.

VICTIM OF A FOOLISH HEART

Words and Music by George Jackson and Mickey Buckins

SOME KIND OF WONDERFUL

Words and Music by Willie Ellison

DIRTY MAN

Words and Music by Robert Miller

I HAD A DREAM

Words and Music by John B. Sebastian

I'VE FALLEN IN LOVE WITH YOU

Words and Music by Carla Thomas

52

ALL THE KING'S HORSES

Words and Music by Aretha Franklin

a tempo

With his arms _____ wrapped all a-round me, ____

it was like a fai - ry - tale. _____ Two

peo - ple ____ so in love, tell me how could this

fail? ____ How could it fail? Oh. ____

FOR THE LOVE OF YOU Pts. 1 & 2

Words and Music by O'Kelly Isley, Marvin Isley, Ronald Isley, Rudolph Isley, Ernie Isley and Chris Jasper

Ad lib. with expression ♩ = c. 85

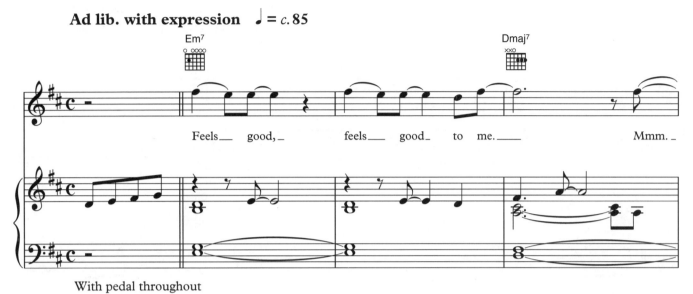

Feels___ good,_ feels___ good_ to me.___ Mmm._

With pedal throughout

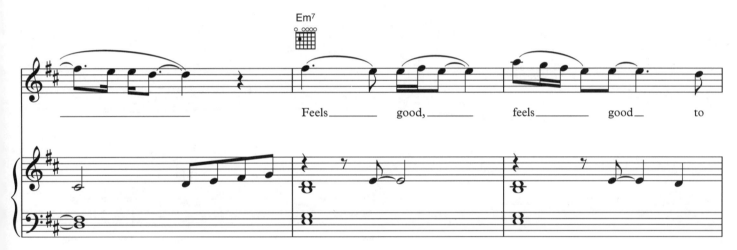

___ Feels_____ good,_____ feels_____ good___ to

me. Oh._____

1. Drift - ing on___ a
2. Love - ly as___ a
3. *See block lyric*

© 1975 EMI April Music Inc and Bovina Music Inc, USA
EMI Songs Ltd, London WC2H 0QY

Ooh, __ to love__ you. __

Ooh, ooh__

3. Paradise I held within
Can't feel insecure again
You're the key
Oh, this I see, this I see, ooh
Now I'm there and I lose my way
Using words to try to say what I feel
I feel that love is free
I know that love is free

I might as well sign my name on a card
Which can say it a whole lot better
Ooh, only time will tell
'Cause it seems that I've done just about all that I can do
I wanna be...

Coda   I just wanna be giving all my love to you
Each and every day
That's when I'll be giving all my love to you

That's all I wanna do
I'm giving all my love to you
You know that I'm living for you